THE DEEP

This book belongs to crew member:

....

write your name here

BLOOMSBURY CHILDREN'S BOOKS
Bloomsbury Publishing Plc
50 Bedford Square, London, WC1B 3DP, UK
BLOOMSBURY, BLOOMSBURY CHILDREN'S BOOKS and the Diana logo are
trademarks of Bloomsbury Publishing Plc
First published in Great Britain 2018 by Bloomsbury Publishing Plc
Text copyright © Bloomsbury Publishing Plc 2018
Image copyright © Technicolor Creative Services USA, Inc. 2018

Based on the multi-award-winning television series THE DEEP, produced by DHX
Media and A Stark Production. Technicolor Creative Services is the primary
rights holder. THE DEEP series is based on the original graphic novels created by
Tom Taylor and James Brouwer.

A catalogue record for this book is available from the British Library

ISBN: 978-1-4088-9885-7

2 4 6 8 10 9 7 5 3 1

Written by Mandy Archer
Text design by Nick Avery
Cover design by James Fraser

With special thanks to Steven Wendland and Marty Kossoff.

With additional thanks to Alison Warner, Pam Kunick-Cohen, Avrill Stark, Robert
Chandler, Tom Taylor, James Brouwer, Wolfgang Bylsma, Trent Carlson, Kristen
Newlands, Anne Loi, Rob Spindley, Sophie Bloomfield and John Lomas-Bullivant.

Printed and bound in Scotland by Bell & Bain Ltd, Glasgow G46 7UQ
All papers used by Bloomsbury Publishing Plc are natural, recyclable products
from wood grown in well managed forests. The manufacturing processes
conform to the environmental regulations of the country of origin

MIX
Paper from
responsible sources
FSC® C007785

To find out more about our authors and books visit www.bloomsbury.com
and sign up for our newsletters
To find out more about THE DEEP visit www.thedeepanimated.com

THE **DEEP**

THE **OFFICIAL HANDBOOK**

BLOOMSBURY
CHILDREN'S BOOKS
LONDON OXFORD NEW YORK NEW DELHI SYDNEY

"My family are explorers. We have been for generations. While others look up to the stars, we know that there are an infinite number of things that shine in the darkness below. There are things lurking in the seas that long ago vanished into myth.

My family are explorers and we explore the Deep..."

CONTENTS

CHAPTER 1
The Truth Is Down There

CHAPTER 2
Nektons And Friends

CHAPTER 3
Exploring The Seas

CHAPTER 4
Pirates, Frenemies And Worse...

CHAPTER 5
Seekers And Protectors

CHAPTER 6
Creatures Of The Deep

CHAPTER 7
Ship's Log

CHAPTER 8
Uncharted Waters

CHAPTER 1
THE TRUTH IS DOWN THERE

INTO THE DEEP

Welcome, Junior Nekton! Your mission has been set. You are going on a journey – a voyage of discovery into the ocean blue. Buckle up – it is going to be quite a ride!

Most of our world is water, and it lies unexplored. Unexplained. Down below us there are mighty mountains, thick forests and valleys so vast they seem to have no end. Every tide brings a new surprise – whirlpools swirl and circle, storms rage and volcanoes roar. This is the world that the Nekton family live in every day. And they are not alone. There are things lurking in the seas that long ago vanished into myth. The Nektons believe that these myths are returning. Secrets are rising out of the abyss.

Antaeus and Fontaine Nekton are the latest in a long line of explorers. Each generation has roamed the ocean, travelling in search of the truth. Back then, Nekton families chartered primitive submersibles. Now Ant, Fontaine and their parents use state-of-the-art technology to further their quest. They believe that somewhere, out there in the blue, the sunken city of Lemuria is waiting – an ancient civilisation that disappeared thousands of years ago.

THE SEA IS THE KEY

Take a deep breath and jump in! What is the ocean really like? It's a place where giant sea beasts snap and prowl, where pirates lurk amidst floating black markets and where undersea quakes shake the seabed. It is also vast – vaster than you could ever imagine...

A MAMMOTH TASK

Humans have only officially explored 5% of the world's oceans so far. The Nektons are pioneers, voyaging into undocumented waters. Ant and Fontaine's journey has only just begun...

A WORLD OF WATER

Think of India, Australia or China – huge nations that are home to millions of people. It would take a lifetime to explore just one of these countries, and yet together they form a small proportion of the world's surface. Around 71% of the world's surface is covered by water. In order to patrol this gigantic kingdom, the Aronnax must navigate incredible distances.

BIGGEST, BRIGHTEST, BEST

Everything in the ocean is super-sized! Just like on land, it has mountain ranges, caves and valleys. The deepest trench is the Mariana in the Pacific Ocean, near the Philippines. In order to reach the bottom, Ant and Fontaine would need to dive down for 11 kilometres straight! The Nektons have explored many other amazing underwater marvels. One of the most colourful is the Great Barrier Reef in Australia – a stunning arc of coral that is so large, it can be seen from the Moon.

MYSTERIOUS CREATURES
Fish that look likes horses, squid that glow in the dark and whales that are bigger than jumbo jets – every Nekton mission brings the chance of a new meeting. Around 94% of the world's creatures dwell here, but scientists haven't even got close to spotting them all. Hundreds of new species are recorded every year. Who or what will Antaeus Nekton come across next?

AN ANCIENT FRIEND
The Nektons have made a pledge to protect the ocean and everything in it. The family understand that the seas are vital for life on Earth. The deep helps to feed us, control our climate and provide the ingredients for our medicines. It also creates at least half of the oxygen we need to breathe.

LIVING HISTORY
Ant Nekton loves exploring sunken shipwrecks and ancient relics.

CHAPTER 2
NEKTONS AND FRIENDS

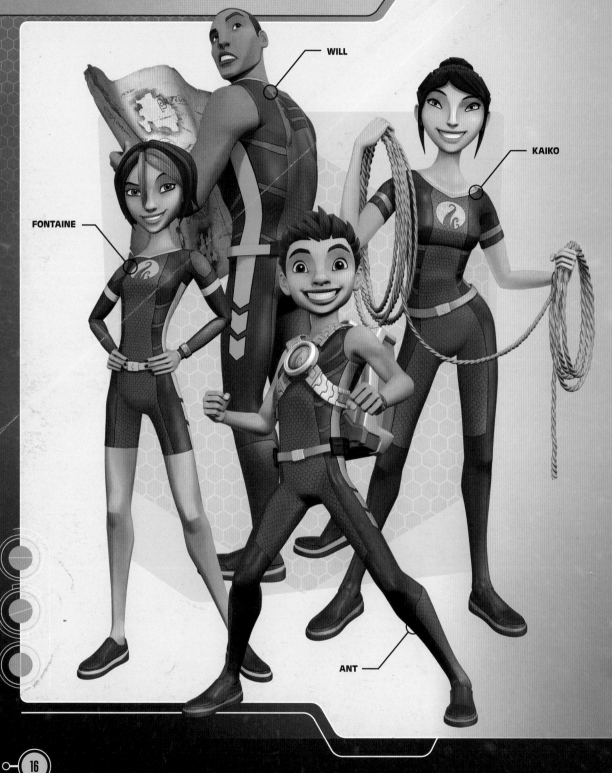

WILL

KAIKO

FONTAINE

ANT

The Nektons are a brilliant team of aquanauts. Ant and his sister Fontaine have lived on-board the Aronnax their whole lives. Their parents Will and Kaiko have taught the family to love the ocean's wonders, but also to respect its overwhelming power.

Whether it's steering the Aronnax through stormy waters, devising an amazing new gadget or going out on a fact-finding dive – the Nektons are in it together. The family are a tight team and everybody has a role to play. Life below the surface can get dangerous, and when there's an emergency Ant and his folks know that they can count on each other one hundred per cent.

The Nektons are just like any regular family... who also happen to be world-famous ocean explorers. Ant and Fontaine get to swim with dolphins, explore undersea caves and follow whale migrations, but that doesn't mean that they don't also have to tidy their bedrooms! Ant fights with his sister every now and then, and he can still get grounded.

Even so, there is no place in the world any of them would rather be. Every day in the deep brings a new adventure. The Nektons often don't know where their next voyage will take them, but they sure can't wait to find out!

ANTAEUS NEKTON

Antaeus Nekton spends most of his life exploring the sea – he is completely at home under the water. Although he is still a boy, Ant has already got an impressive knowledge of oceanography, the ability to design and build gadgets his family never knew they needed and some jaw-dropping survival skills.

The sparky twelve-year-old gets a total buzz from swimming up close to gigantic sea creatures, exploring sunken caves... and annoying his big sister, Fontaine! Ant's bravery holds no bounds. When there is an emergency, he leaps in first and thinks later. Sometimes Ant's recklessness gives his mum and dad a few grey hairs, but they trust in his uncanny ability to think under pressure.

Nature Boy
Ant loves all undersea life – including super-sized water bugs! Marine biology is his favourite subject.

JORANGE
Special pet carrier for Ant's fish, Jeffrey.

WRISTBAND
Acts as a communicator and enables access to key data from the Aronnax computer.

SUPER-LITE WETSUIT
Allows speed and movement both in and out of the water.

Count On Me
Ant is a key member of the Aronnax crew. He may be young, but he never shies away from danger. He swims towards it instead!

Eyes Wide Open

When it comes to the mysteries of the Deep, Ant is willing to accept the strange and the incredible. He believes that every theory has the potential to be true, until proven otherwise. In the ocean, he argues, anything is possible.

AGE: 12

HEIGHT: 136 cm

LIKES: Exploring and inventing

DISLIKES: Being bored

KIT: Ant loves all tech, but he is especially proud of the Shadow Knight. He invented it himself.

CLASSIFIED INTEL

Ant won't admit it, but his underwear is covered in fish symbols!

FAMILY FIRST

Ant loves being a Nekton. OK, he's not so great at tidying his room, and Fontaine is sure that it's him who keeps stealing all the cookies, but hey – nobody's perfect!

"Have faith in the fish!"

JEFFREY

BLANK STARE
Don't be fooled, this fish is smart!

He might be tiny, but only a crazy pirate would underestimate this fish! Jeffrey is more than Ant's beloved pet – he is a fully-fledged member of Team Nekton.

This little guy is brave, loyal and proof that some fish do have more than a three-second memory. Jeffrey also has a knack of swimming into the right place at the right time, spotting crucial details that others have overlooked. Ant takes his pal everywhere with him, even when that means carrying a fish tank on his back...

SKY-BLUE FINS
Jeffrey is a first-rate swimmer.

DATA FILE

AGE: 2

HEIGHT: 10 cm

LIKES: Fish snacks

DISLIKES: Predators

KIT: Ant has designed a special 'fishcam' for Jeffrey to wear – a mini digital camera. He also has his own Jeffrey Knight.

CLASSIFIED INTEL
Ant once saved Jeffrey's life, and the pair have been inseparable ever since.

Friendly Fish
Jeffrey is a great judge of character! Naturally curious, he often makes new friends when he goes out exploring with Ant.

"Jeffrey is practically a genius by fish standards."

FONTAINE NEKTON

Fontaine is Ant's older, and she would say wiser, sister. She's a clued-up, smart teenager who sometimes despairs of her maverick little bro. Ant and Fontaine are like chalk and chowder. Even though the siblings bicker and bait each other all day long, underneath all that rivalry Fontaine and Ant share an unbreakable bond. As Fontaine would say, you can't live in someone's pocket 24/7 without them getting under your skin just a little bit...

NEKTON BADGE
Worn with pride ever since she can remember.

CROPPED WETSUIT
Flexible and enables super quick wet-to-dry transition.

A true Nekton, Fontaine is passionate about the survival of the ocean. She is a strong swimmer and a gifted navigator. She is also Kaiko's natural apprentice, soaking up knowledge like a sponge. Fontaine analyses situations before diving in. She takes action in her own time and on her terms, and more often than not her shrewd thinking has saved the Aronnax from deep-sea doom.

AMPHIBIOUS SHOES
Protective sole for safe seabed exploration, cushioned for sprinting on deck.

PLAY IT COOL

When she needs to escape, Fontaine puts on her headphones and gets lost in music. She plays a range of instruments, but she loves rocking out on her guitar best of all.

TABLET PHONE
State of the art, designed by Professor Fiction.

AMAZING GAZING

The sights of the deep bring out Fontaine's sense of wonder. Who could watch a whale migration, peep inside a sea cave or explore a rainbow coral field without getting excited?

KAIKO NEKTON

HAIR TIED BACK
To avoid accidents with Aronnax machinery.

FULL-BODY WETSUIT
Kaiko's choice for working on the bridge.

COLOUR-CODED STRIPES
Every Nekton wetsuit is unique, fitted to the individual.

PANELLED SECTIONS
Allows free movement and increases comfort.

Kaiko Nekton is fiercely protective of her family. She's a born leader, who won't hesitate to speak up if she thinks any of her loved ones are under threat. As well as being mum to Ant and Fontaine, Kaiko is the pilot of the Aronnax.

She's a skilled mechanic with the ability to think around practical problems. If there's a solution out there, Kaiko won't give up until she finds it! It makes her stubborn, but effective. She also has a knack for assessing a situation and spotting potential threats that others are yet to see. When the pressure's on, Kaiko's word is final. Kaiko spent her own childhood with her head underwater, snorkelling and scuba diving at her parents' Marine Protection Reserve. This inspired her to study Marine Biology and Conservation – a subject that has turned her into a passionate eco-warrior.

Dice With Danger
Just when Kaiko thinks that she has seen it all, the ocean offers up a staggering new surprise.

FAMILY VALUES

Kaiko met her husband, Will, during her marine studies. She can see a lot of Will's scientific curiosity in Ant, too. She is proud to be part of the Nekton family.

AGE: 42

HEIGHT: 168 cm

LIKES: Tinkering in the Aronnax engine room

DISLIKES: Anything that puts her family in danger

KIT: The Aronnax is Kaiko's pride and joy. She is constantly working on the sub to keep it in top condition.

CLASSIFIED INTEL

Kaiko has always loved taking things apart to find out how they work. This is probably where Ant gets his tech ability from – it's in the genes.

LET'S GO!

Kaiko knows how to push the Aronnax to its absolute max! She can make the sub dodge, speed and dive, all whilst managing the comms to the Knights outside.

"Nekton family, strap yourselves in!"

WILLIAM NEKTON

If you asked Fontaine and Ant to sum up their dad in two words, they'd say 'gentle giant'. William Nekton is as strong as a seal, athletic and incredibly fit, but he's happiest when he's got his head stuck in a map or an old manuscript.

Will spent his youth in the Coral Triangle, where he grew up alongside the children of the Bajau Sea Nomads. It was here that his curious nature surfaced. Will is fascinated about the past, and what it can tell us about the future. He spends his free-time studying archaeology, cartography and ancient languages.

For Will however, the ocean isn't about maps that already exist, it's about the secrets that lie beyond them. Will has devoted his life to searching for Lemuria, a quest that he shares with his whole family. At home, Will is just like any regular dad – when he's not peering through his glasses at a parchment or exploring in the Mag Knight, you'll find him doing the dishes or checking up on Ant and Fontaine's homework.

SLEEVELESS WETSUIT
Cropped at the top of the arm, just like Ant's.

LEMURIAN CHART
This Nekton is rarely seen without a map in one hand.

MUSCLE-FIT FABRIC
Will works out regularly – fitness is essential on-board the Aronnax.

EASY-CHANGE FOOTWEAR
Smart shoes can be instantly clicked into flippers when Will wants to go diving.

AGE: 44
HEIGHT: 192 cm
LIKES: Reading maps and swimming
DISLIKES: Pirates
KIT: The Aronnax vault holds Will's most precious collection – rare Lemurian artefacts discovered during his travels through the ocean.

CLASSIFIED INTEL
Will is never one to brag, but he was once an Olympic swimmer! He still loves to swim every day.

SAFETY FIRST
Will has faith in his family's abilities, but his first instinct is to shield them from danger. Before taking action, he is quick to assess the stakes and set the boundaries of each mission.

OCEAN EXPLORER
Every day offers a new opportunity for Will to uncover new clues and discover new treasures. He prefers to dive in and study sea animals and plants in their natural habitats.

Father's Footsteps
It was Will's father who first started the journey towards finding Lemuria. Will is determined to see it through!

"Myths have to start somewhere."

PROFESSOR FICTION

AGE: 31

HEIGHT: 176 cm (with hair)

LIKES: Building mechanical devices with Ant

DISLIKES: Losing his wrench

KIT: Professor Fiction is tech-obsessed – how could he possibly choose one piece of kit over all the rest?

CLASSIFIED INTEL

Professor Fiction spends most of his time working at the Nekton's secret island base. The precise location is too confidential to print.

PRISM SET GLASSES
The Prof's glasses are reinforced to double up as lab goggles.

LAB COAT
Burns, shocks, minor explosions – Professor Fiction gets through dozens of these a month.

ODD SOCKS
Colourful and quirky, just like the man himself.

Ant and his family can't protect the whole world's oceans by themselves – a network of top scientists, programmers and mechanics support them behind the scenes from Nekton Headquarters, a base somewhere in the South Pacific. Genius inventor Professor Fiction runs the entire unit.

His unrivalled understanding of engineering, combined with his wild imagination, means that he has spent most of his life working in secret. He is responsible for all the gadgets aboard the Aronnax, but the Professor has brand new eureka moments every single day. When it comes to tech, he and Ant are as excitable as each other. The pair love swapping ideas and playing with prototypes. Experimenting is the only way to learn!

"Be careful, Ant! The modifications are experimental."

NEREUS

WHITE BEARD
Grown so long that Nereus has to tie it up.

PLAIN CLOTHES
When he's not wearing his Guardian robes, Nereus prefers to blend in with the crowd.

STAFF
A useful walking stick, or maybe a tool that's much more powerful?

Nereus is a mystery, wrapped in an enigma, wrapped in a beard. The strange old man has a habit of appearing at surprising moments, often when the Nekton family least expect it.

Ant is amused by Nereus' eccentric ways and funny practical jokes, but there is more to him than first meets the eye. Fontaine doesn't know what to make of his odd behaviour, and she's not entirely sure whether he has the Nektons' best interests at heart. He certainly seems to know more than he is letting on about Lemuria. Indeed, he claims to be one of the Guardians – a secret group dedicated to preserving Lemurian culture. So what really is Nereus' story? That tale is still to be told...

DATA FILE

AGE: Unknown

HEIGHT: 164 cm

LIKES: Saying cryptic things

DISLIKES: Traitors. Trust is everything.

KIT: An old wooden rowing boat does Nereus just fine. He's been using it for more years than he can count. Why change now?

CLASSIFIED INTEL
Nobody knows Nereus' true age. Including Nereus himself.

CHAPTER 3
EXPLORING THE SEAS

THE ARONNAX

The underwater home of the Nektons is the envy of submariners worldwide. Every section of this craft is the product of cutting-edge technology – designed to be energy-efficient, streamlined and capable of astonishing underwater velocity. It is, quite simply, the largest and most effective ocean vehicle on the planet. Welcome on-board the Aronnax...

THE ARONNAX

LENGTH: 250 m
WEIGHT: 50,000 tonnes
DEPTH: Can dive to 2,000 m
SPEED: Up to 80 km/hr
FUNCTION: The Nekton family's home

FEATURES: Equipped with a range of ancillary and defence vehicles. The Aronnax is a peaceful vessel – it carries no weapons.

THE ARONNAX

The world's largest submarine is a marvel of engineering. Three times longer than any military sub on the globe, the Aronnax uses biomimicry to operate effectively in its ocean setting. Professor Fiction turned to nature when he designed its curved, whale-like shape, creating a machine that could move in the water with a grace that belies its vast size.

PANORAMIC 180° PILOT VIEW

GIANT RUDDER AND STABILIZING WINGS

MOON POOL CHAMBER

BOARDING HATCH

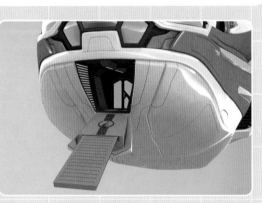

AUTOMATED GANGPLANK

LONGER THAN FIVE FOOTBALL FIELDS

BRIDGE AND COMMAND CENTRE

EXTERIOR EJECTION PORTS FOR SURFACE VEHICLES

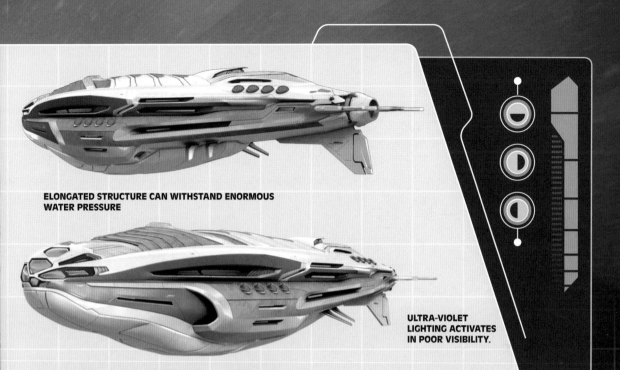

ELONGATED STRUCTURE CAN WITHSTAND ENORMOUS WATER PRESSURE

ULTRA-VIOLET LIGHTING ACTIVATES IN POOR VISIBILITY.

The Aronnax is a sensitive and responsive sub to command – navigating extreme weather conditions and hostile environments with ease. Its elite radar system can detect hazards and activity from hundreds of kilometres away, warning when intervention is required. Holographic screens display an array of views of the outside world, keeping the Nektons one step ahead of the game.

DOUBLE-TITANIUM HULL

COMMAND AND CONTROL

When the Nektons stand on the bridge of the Aronnax and gaze out through its vast windows, they have an immersive, whale's eye view of the ocean.

The interior of the Aronnax is as unique as the outside. Despite its phenomenal marine capabilities, the sub has been designed so that a small crew of four can operate it, backed up by remote links to Professor Fiction's on-call command centre. Will captains the ship, Kaiko is the pilot, Fontaine is in charge of the navigational instruments, leaving Ant to man the periscope and a whole lot more. The engine of the Aronnax is efficient, eco-friendly and super-responsive, designed to maximize the Nektons' pledge to respond and rescue any human, or creature, in trouble at sea.

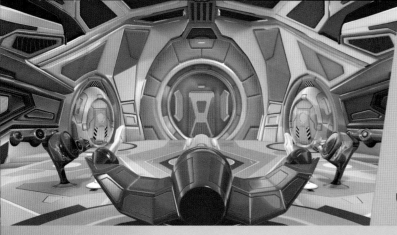

THE BRIDGE

The bridge is the hub of the sub – an open level fitted with three seated control stations. The main computer deck blinks with radar screens, digital depth gauges, mapping data and live engine analysis. Pop-up hologram screens allow the Nektons to scan for USOs – Unidentified Submerged Objects.

THE SERVER ROOM

The computer network on-board the Aronnax is cutting edge, but the mainframe is constantly being reviewed, refined and updated. The computer is powered by a massive server located in the base of the sub.

ENGINE ROOM

Kaiko is a frequent visitor to the engine room, although Ant is often right beside her! The pair enjoy getting their hands dirty, oiling the mechanics and devising on-the-spot fixes when the sub incurs a breach.

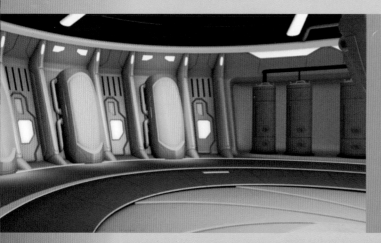

THE MOON POOL

The Moon Pool chamber houses the Nektons' fleet of underwater vehicles and equipment, including the Rover and the Knights. A kaleidoscopic airlock covers the pool, able to open and close within seconds when the family needs to dock or shut out intruders.

LIVING AND LEARNING

As well as being a top-notch exploration vessel, the Aronnax is also the Nektons' home. Outside the expected operations and research facilities, the sub has five bedrooms, a library, a kitchen plus plenty of space for Ant and Fontaine to kick back and relax.

The Nekton kids are home-schooled, and so the sub has been equipped with interactive learning resources, a fully working laboratory and study areas. The Aronnax is even big enough to cope with Ant's boundless energy – when he's not out diving, he can go for a run, kick a ball around or ride his skateboard along the vessel's corridors. Everything inside the Aronnax is designed to cope with the practicalities of life underwater. Tools and utensils are stowed away in fitted recesses that shut instantly if the ocean becomes stormy and rough. Air quality and temperature is regulated 24/7.

GETTING AROUND

The areas inside the Aronnax are connected by a maze of elevators and corridors. Many have been constructed along the exterior wall of the sub, enjoying breathtaking views of the ocean outside. Filtered tubes mounted along the walls allow Jeffrey to swim between the different zones.

THE LIBRARY

The library has been installed for everyone's use, but Will spends many hours here working on private study. The round chamber houses his collection of ancient sea charts and rare Lemurian artefacts. A panel of holographic screens line the walls to one side.

ANT'S BEDROOM

The Nektons' bedrooms are functional, but they do have some home comforts, too! Ant's shelves are lined with books and souvenirs, and there's a flatscreen TV for gaming and watching movies. The lighting can be switched off from his bed if Ant wants to lie-in!

THE WHITE KNIGHT

ENHANCED MOBILITY
Suit self-propels through water.

UNDER PRESSURE
The White Knight provides protection from the incredible pressure at the bottom of the ocean. Ant and his family can swim at depths most aquanauts never get to experience.

EXTRA ARMS
The White Knight's robotic arms can wield great strength.

JOINTED PARTS
Suit is fully jointed to increase dexterity.

ALL-TERRAIN VISION
A heads-up display inside the helmet guides the pilot.

The Knights are single-person, armoured diving suits. They allow the Nektons to go everywhere underwater, encased and defended against hostile sea encounters, extreme weather conditions and treacherous terrain. The White Knight was the very first suit created for the Nektons. It is designed for deep-sea exploration.

Ever-Ready
The frame of the White Knight is encased in protective steel that won't erode in seawater.

RETRIEVE AND REBUILD

Professor Fiction built the White Knight to go to work! It is able to handle tools and carry out external maintenance on the Aronnax. The suit's built-in laser cutter can sear through sheet metal with ease.

LOW LIGHTING

The suit is equipped with special lighting and glow features to facilitate deep dives in waters with zero visibility.

THE SHADOW KNIGHT

Take a long look at the Shadow Knight while you have the chance – this diving suit has a habit of disappearing from scanners and radar screens! The Shadow Knight is a stealth vehicle. The equipment is small, fast and built for camouflage. It is almost exclusively used by Ant.

360° MOVEMENT
Flexible shoulders allow arms to stretch and turn.

Speed Suit
The Shadow Knight is able to travel faster than a mako shark.

REINFORCED SLEEVES
Aquanaut's arms slot in here.

LOW SHEEN SHELL
Grey metallic colouring is almost invisible in water.

FIT AND LOCK
The Shadow Knight's hands are designed to interface with tools and rescue equipment.

Downwardly Mobile
Weighing in at one tonne, the Shadow Knight is one of the lightest, but most nimble Knights in the Nekton fleet.

CLOAKING ABILITY

When the Nektons need to go undercover, this suit can be switched to 'stealth mode'. The Shadow Knight is able to disappear completely from all sonar and radar operating in the surrounding area.

PASSION PROJECT

The Shadow Knight concept was Ant's idea. He and Professor Fiction worked on the development in secret for months before they finally revealed the suit to the rest of the Nekton family.

SAFETY FIRST

Ant safety tested the Shadow Knight with a real-life rescue. When a long-distance kayaker found herself in trouble at sea, the suit was the only piece of kit enabled and ready to save her. It passed with flying colours!

PROBE AND EXPLORE

The Shadow Knight's cloaking ability allows it to roam the ocean undisturbed by passing subs or surveillance craft.

THE SWAMP KNIGHT

The Swamp Knight is sturdy, robust and mega-powerful. The Nektons' only totally amphibious diving suit can function equally well on land as it can underwater. This is a suit for heavy-duty operations only – digging out flooded caves, marching through boggy marshes or confronting giant crocodiles. The big green titan is a true marvel of mechanical engineering.

GRABBING CLAMPS
Digits can grasp and lift heavy loads.

HEAD ACTIVATION
The steering is controlled by head movement alone.

CARRY-ONS
The Knight has extra in-built storage compartments.

Extra Strength
The suit possesses such powerful thrusters, it can take time to learn how to control it safely.

Driving Force
What the Swamp Knight hasn't got in speed, it makes up for in three tonnes of sheer bulk.

BODY ARMOUR
Super-strength armour is even able to crush rock.

MAKE A CONNECTION

When the Nektons need to stick together, Will turns to the Swamp Knight. Its magnetic anchor cables can shoot out and lasso objects being swept away in the currents.

INCREDIBLE RESCUES

The Swamp Knight boasts awesome load-bearing capabilities. It can tow several times its own body weight, even when cutting through churning waters. It has proved itself to be a huge asset during rescue operations.

THE MAG KNIGHT

GRAPPLING HOOKS
Flexible claws can be launched at an instant's notice.

Only one Nekton Knight is stronger than the Swamp Knight –the mighty Mag! The Mag Knight operates like a portable, wearable power crane. With super strength, grappling hooks and tough magnet projectiles among its built-in tools, this knight is made for utility. It is the least agile of the group.

SMART TECH
The Mag Knight weighs the same as an average car.

Grounding Force
The Mag Knight is able to anchor other objects down using its magnetic cables and feet.

GIANT TOOLKIT
Drills, winches and flares are fitted all over the Mag Knight's body.

SWIVEL AND SORT
Hands rotate at the push of a button.

Mag Materials
Despite its size and extreme stability, the Mag Knight is constructed from lightweight metal.

BIG HITTER

The Mag Knight is Will Nekton's favourite Knight because it is the biggest and strongest. He selects the Mag Knight when he needs to carry out heavy-duty maintenance work, such as lifting, tunnelling and welding.

Brace Yourself
In extreme situations, this Knight is the last to leave, securing the area until everyone else has evacuated.

THE MIMIC KNIGHT

It's easy to sense the inspiration behind Fontaine's flexible diving suit – it has the tail and form of a mermaid! The Mimic Knight is fast and agile, allowing the wearer to integrate with sea creatures. This capacity for interaction makes the Mimic Knight perfect for researching marine mammal dynamics.

FLIPPERS
Built for manoeuvring amongst dolphins and other sealife.

TAIL BLEND
Suit changes colour to match the environment or creature it swims with.

COMMS LINK
Ensures constant contact with Nekton control.

SURPRISE!

Fontaine and Professor Fiction developed the Mimic Knight in secret. Before it was officially unveiled, Fontaine swam past the Aronnax wearing seaweed 'hair'. Ant was fooled into believing he'd seen a *real* mermaid!

THE JEFFREY KNIGHT

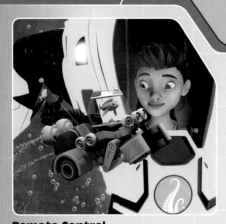

When Ant got fed up with leaving his pet at home every time he went out, he decided to take action. The Jeffrey Knight was the result – a miniature craft with the ability to take a little fish anywhere and everywhere! The Knight is not much bigger than a can of paint, but it has opened up a whole new world of adventure...

Remote Control
The Jeffrey Knight comes with a remote, but the clever fish can work the technology all by himself.

HAND-MADE
Ant put together the Jeffrey Knight using objects that he managed to salvage from around the Aronnax. The four purple wheels were borrowed from Fontaine's skateboard.

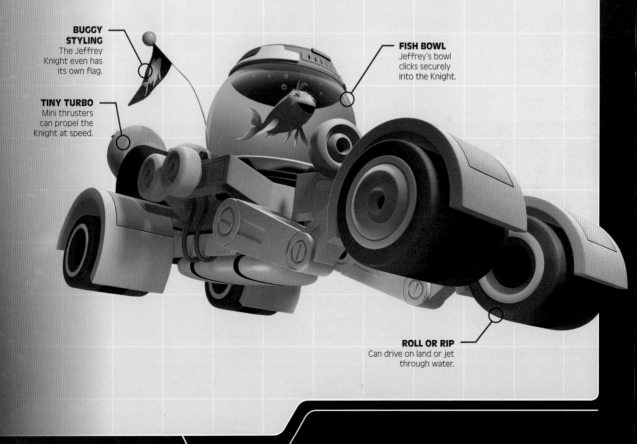

BUGGY STYLING
The Jeffrey Knight even has its own flag.

TINY TURBO
Mini thrusters can propel the Knight at speed.

FISH BOWL
Jeffrey's bowl clicks securely into the Knight.

ROLL OR RIP
Can drive on land or jet through water.

"Buckle up!"

THE ROVER

A small submersible capable of diving to far greater depths than the Aronnax, the Rover can also navigate small trenches, caves and ravines that the submarine simply can't reach. The Rover has large strong arms that can move submerged shipwrecks and other impediments.

ANTI-CRACK SCREEN
Reinforced glass protects the crew from extreme water pressure.

AERODYNAMIC BODY
Maximizes dive capacity.

RETRACTABLE ARMS
Arms stretch to 4.6 metres when fully extended.

MULTI-FUNCTIONAL PORT
Provides light and works as an underwater speaker.

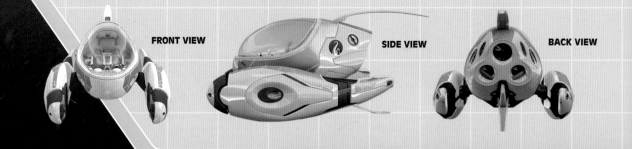

FRONT VIEW

SIDE VIEW

BACK VIEW

QUICK DISPATCH

The mini sub has a pressurized cabin that can house up to five passengers. The Rover can be operational within seconds.

THE SEA IS THE KEY

The Nektons used the Rover to explore the waters surrounding the remote island of Tartaruga. It was there that Ant made an important discovery in the quest for Lemuria. The sub gave him an amazing view of the ocean.

DEEP DIVER

The Rover is fitted with bright halogen lights, allowing it to explore the darkest depths of the ocean. It is one of the only manned submarines in the world capable of diving to the deepest part of the sea, the Mariana Trench.

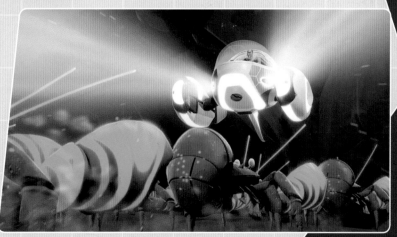

THE SOLAR SKIS

Not all ocean exploration happens underwater. As a result, the Nekton family have researched several craft that can operate on the sea surface... and above it. The Solar Skis are sleek, eco-friendly, single-person jet skis that can leap over waves at astonishing speed.

FRONT VIEW

Fast And Friendly
The Solar Skis are almost silent. They leave no polluting oil or petrol in the water behind them.

BACK VIEW

JUMP START

The skis can be launched quickly from the Aronnax. Each one is fired with the rider already seated from wide tubes on the side of the submarine. When necessary, a passenger can sit behind each rider for short distances.

POWER STEERING
Solar Skis are responsive and easy to handle.

SOLAR PANELS
Capture and store charge.

FOOTBOARD
Easy to climb onto during ocean rescues.

CURVED DESIGN
Enables low friction movement through launch tubes.

THE JETBOAT

FRONT VIEW

BACK VIEW

The Jetboat is lightning fast and comes with a stunning array of gadgets. Like the Solar Skis, the Jetboat is solar-powered, but it is much, much faster. This is the vehicle the Nektons use when they receive surface mayday signals that require urgent action.

SUPER-BOUYANCY
Frame shape makes the jetboat almost impossible to capsize.

RETRACTABLE SCREEN
Cockpit can be sealed during inclement weather.

Day Trippers
The Jetboat is the perfect vehicle for trips and excursions. The Nektons also use it as a launch for diving and snorkelling in shallow waters.

MULTI-VALVE POWER
The Jetboat's engine is silent, but super-efficient.

CHAPTER 4
PIRATES, FRENEMIES AND WORSE...

MEET THE PIRATES

Jolly Rogers, pieces of eight and stolen booty are not only the stuff of storybooks – buccaneers are an ever-present threat to peace and stability in the ocean. Captain Hammerhead and his crew are a new breed of underwater pirate, an unruly mob who seek only to pillage, and never to protect.

Known as the 'Dark Orca', the gang are ruled by the dreaded Captain Hammerhead. His children, Smiling Finn and Mad Madeline, live on his submarine too, ready to thwart the Nektons at every twist and turn. They're all experts at sniffing out trouble. If there is treasure to be snatched, they'll dive in and take it – not caring who or what gets caught in the crossfire.

CAPTAIN HAMMERHEAD

A true pirate's pirate, Captain Hammerhead rules the Dark Orca with a fierce scowl and a booming voice. He is rude, stinky and obsessed with money and gold. Hammerhead loves to win, especially when he is taking on the Nektons.

When there's an SOS, the Captain is full of bluster, but somehow things never quite go to plan. Despite his gruff exterior, perhaps the pirate isn't quite as heartless as he makes out? The old seadog is also a dad to two children – a job he finds harder than handling a sub full of rascals and buccaneers.

TATTOO
No one can call themselves a true pirate without one.

GOLD RINGS
All snatched, none of them paid for.

DATA FILE

AGE: 43
HEIGHT: 189 cm
LIKES: Stealing and looting
DISLIKES: The Nektons
KIT: The Dark Orca. The Captain's gloomy, whale-shaped submarine is his pride and joy.

CLASSIFIED INTEL
No one knows what happened to Captain Hammerhead's wife. Could she have been lost at sea?

HEAVY BOOTS
For stomping up and down the deck of the Dark Orca.

"Get me that treasure!"

SMILING FINN

CHEEKY GRIN
Always on
show, especially
if Fontaine's
nearby.

EARRING
Just the right
accessory for
a teenage
rebel.

OLD JEANS
Pirates rarely
bother with
doing the
laundry.

Can We Be Friends?
At first, Finn and Fontaine cannot stand each other.
Over time however, both begin to realise that they
have more in common than they first thought.

Smiling Finn is Captain Hammerhead's eldest child. He is fit, charming, able and... bored. Finn does not share his dad's passion for plunder, despite his abilities.

In a family of scoundrels, Finn is the
misfit. He loves the thrill of the ocean
deep and has all the skills to be a
famous pirate, it's just the ruthless and
bloodthirsty part of the gig that he's not
so happy with.

◄ **DATA FILE**

AGE:	16
HEIGHT:	171 cm
LIKES:	Fontaine Nekton
DISLIKES:	The tough stuff about being a pirate
KIT:	Finn gets a buzz from solo piloting the Red Claw.

CLASSIFIED INTEL
Finn keeps hold of a communicator
that belongs to Fontaine. Sometimes
he uses it to allow the Nektons to
track him.

"It was kinda nice to avoid certain doom with you."

MAD MADELINE

Captain Hammerhead does have one child who is completely devoted to his cause – his youngest child, 'Mad' Madeline. The rascal-in-training loves everything about pirating, and is keen to prove herself as one of the absolute worst. If there's a dirty job to do, Madeline wants in!

Madeline has loathed Ant from day one. The Nekton drives her crazy every time he mocks her pirate credentials. He is always first to remind Madeline that she can't be a proper buccaneer – she doesn't even have a parrot! Madeline has sworn to get her own back on her rival, even if it takes years...

WILD EYES
Madeline is ALWAYS angry.

BANGLES AND BEADS
Treasures collected on her many pirate adventures.

BELT BUCKLE
Made for a fully-grown man, but it belongs to Madeline now.

DATA FILE

AGE: 10

HEIGHT: 136 cm

LIKES: Being a pirate

DISLIKES: Ant Nekton

KIT: Madeline regularly fights with Finn over the Red Claw. She thinks it's the best sub in the sea.

CLASSIFIED INTEL
When she was tiny, Madeline's mum used to dress her up in a mermaid outfit.

"I'll make you walk the plank, you scurvy dog!"

DANNY-BOY

MECHANICAL MIND?
Danny-Boy pretends to know a lot about mechanics.

When the Captain goes off to wrestle sharks or snatch treasure maps, he trusts his submarine to Danny-Boy. The Dark Orca's second-in-command is experienced, wily... and allergic to danger. If Danny-Boy spots peril coming his way, he swerves in the opposite direction. He'd much rather be hidden away in the control room eating a plate of kippers with his feet up.

Danny-Boy tries to please Captain Hammerhead, but that task is easier said than done. As well as piloting the Dark Orca, he is also the sub's chief mechanic and pirate gadget fixer.

WATERPROOF JACKET
It can get cold down in the Dark Orca's engine room.

GUMBOOTS
Come in handy every time the sub springs a leak.

Tight Spot
During his time on-board the Dark Orca, Danny-Boy has escaped from many unpleasant situations.

DOLOS

BEANY HAT
For dark nights patrolling the boards of the Black Market.

SECRET DOCUMENTS
Dolos is gifted at translating ancient symbols.

SEAMAN'S OUTFIT
Allows Dolos to blend in when he goes above the surface.

Only one person can be sure who's side Dolos is on, and that's Dolos himself. He's an old acquaintance of Will and Kaiko from their college days, proving himself to be a genius at interpreting different languages. Now he sells information, trading in facts and rumours. Dolos will hawk anything for a price.

MAN OF MYSTERY

Dolos lives amongst the Floating Black Market. Hundreds of traders meet at secret times and in secret places, linking boats, flotillas and rafts to create a dangerous moving marketplace. He lurks there in the shadows with Hydra, his pet octopus.

"Everything belongs to me if I want it. I'm a pirate!"

THE DARK ORCA

The Dark Orca is the anti-Aronnax and an ominous-looking presence in the water. The pirates' submarine has a skull and crossbones painted on the bottom of its hull – a warning to all who come near. It is fitted with a unique set of grappling hooks capable of dragging a ship under the surface.

THE DARK ORCA

LENGTH: 160 m

WEIGHT: 48,000 tonnes

DEPTH: Can dive to 1,000 m

SPEED: Up to 40 km/hr

FUNCTION: The pirates' home and fighting machine

FEATURES: Shaped like a killer whale, the Dark Orca is equipped with an assortment of weapons.

THE DARK ORCA

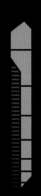

The dark, brooding shape of the Dark Orca is feared by sailors all over the world. Some swear that tales of a terrible pirate submarine are the stuff of myth, but this hulking iron monster is very real. The vessel lurks in deep waters, ready to rise up and attack any foes that try to pass above.

SURFACE ENTRY CHAMBER

FOUR REAR THRUSTERS

PAIRED BALANCE FLIPPERS

Cold Comfort

The Dark Orca is a harsh environment to live in 24/7. The walls are riveted with bolts, and the corridors are lined with clanking metal service pipes.

PERISCOPE

CAPTAIN'S CONTROL ROOM

BILGE PIPE

FIGHTING FIT

The Dark Orca combines stolen technology with old-fashioned sailing equipment. Captain Hammerhead relies on a steering wheel and brute force to guide his sub through the ocean. Over the years, the vessel has incurred many knocks.

Moon Pool
The crew enter and exit the Dark Orca through a portal tucked in the underside of the vessel. The pirates use the moon pool to launch the Red Claw and the 'Super Knight'.

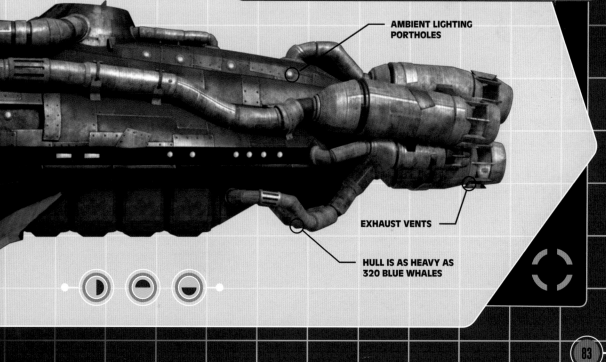

AMBIENT LIGHTING PORTHOLES

EXHAUST VENTS

HULL IS AS HEAVY AS 320 BLUE WHALES

THE RED CLAW

The Nektons have the Rover... the pirates have the Red Claw. The noisy, diesel-powered submersible has been rebuilt countless times. The Red Claw is designed to snatch, grab or dig for treasure. The scratches and scars all over its shell reveal its other function – to fight Captain Hammerhead's enemies.

CARBON DIOXIDE VENT
Helps maintain oxygen circulation inside the cockpit.

PNEUMATIC CLAWS
Useful for scavenging and combat.

STEEL SHELL
Modelled on a marine lobster.

PATCH IT UP

Danny-Boy has to repair the Red Claw regularly because the vessel's heavy steel parts are prone to snapping if placed under pressure. The submersible weighs in at four tonnes without any crew members on-board.

SERRATED PINCERS
Increase grip capability.

THE 'SUPER KNIGHT'

When Captain Hammerhead spotted Ant soaring through the sea in the Shadow Knight, he decided to build a diving suit for himself. Cue the 'Super Knight' – a rusty metal monster that weighs as much as a giant hippopotamus!

FITTED TOOLS
For repairs, and fighting.

OVER-SIZED COMPONENTS
At its full height, the Knight measures 3.3 metres.

JOINTED FINGERS
Each hand can grab, twist and clench.

Heavy Weight
The Captain's suit was built out of scrap steel, making it much heavier than the Nektons' Knights.

WIDE BASE
Broad feet provide stability, but can hinder floating.

CONGER

Sebastian Conger shuns the outside world, preferring to live alone in the middle of the ocean. He is an eccentric – a collector of rare and obscure things, including maps, trinkets and animals. But are Conger's affairs as harmless as they appear? The Nektons suspect not. They've witnessed his ruthlessness enough times to realise that Conger is slimier than seaweed.

Secret Hideaway
Conger is careful to plot a course for his home that avoids any territorial waters, allowing him to operate outside international rules and conventions.

The wealthy businessman can be tricky to pin down. Conger owns a giant portable home that constantly moves around the seafloor. He uses hired henchmen to spy, steal and raid, in order to build up his treasure vault. He is a poacher and a thief, but Conger may have even bigger plans in mind.

IMPRESSIVE INTELLECT
Conger is a gifted scientist, but his skills are not put to good use.

GIANT GALAPAGOS TORTOISE
One of the rare species pursued by Conger.

DEVIL DANIELS

First-Class Fraud
On his show, Daniels loves to boast about his ocean adventures. He'll do anything to get likes from his fans! Off-camera, his British accent, and his courage, soon begin to slip.

Devil Daniels likes to introduce himself as a flashy British adventurer, big-game trophy hunter and celebrity blogger. But when the cameras are off, Ant and his family get to see the real deal. Daniels is a callous headline seeker – a media-savvy American who refuses to let the truth get in the way of a good story.

Devil Daniels will do anything, no matter how reckless, in the name of 'entertainment'. He likes to film himself cruising in a speedboat called the Monster Hunter, pretending to pursue deadly krakens, sharks and sea serpents. But when danger really does loom near, Daniels is always the first sailor to jump ship.

BRANDED KIT
The star has his own range of T-shirts, caps and action figures.

RUGGED GOOD LOOKS
Daniels is all about appearance!

ALPHEUS BENTHOS

Alpheus Benthos is a cunning, powerful and hopelessly spoilt young man. He traverses the globe in his submarine, equipped with state-of-the-art technology and an incredible satellite map of the ocean floor. He's a man on a mission to rediscover Lemuria and harness its astonishing power.

Alpheus was once friends with Nereus, but now he remains loyal only to himself. His ambition holds no bounds. It would all be so simple, too – if Alpheus' archrival, Ant Nekton, didn't keep turning up to ruin his plans.

DIGITAL CIRCUITRY
Designed to be responsive to Alpheus' movement.

BUILT-IN COMMUNICATOR
Connects Alpheus to Aria, the AI system on his submarine.

NEOPRENE WETSUIT
Fitted with integrated body armour.

DATA FILE

AGE: 18

HEIGHT: 170 cm (with hair)

LIKES: To rule the world!

DISLIKES: Losing out to Ant Nekton

KIT: Alpheus operates a sleek, single-crew submarine called the Stinger. It runs on nuclear fusion.

CLASSIFIED INTEL
Alpheus is a descendant of the rogue line of ancient people that fought the Queen of Lemuria.

"Antaeus Nekton... You are destined to be my nemesis."

CHAPTER 5
SEEKERS AND PROTECTORS

WORLD OCEANS AUTHORITY

The Nektons and the leaders of the World Oceans Authority have a complicated relationship. Sometimes the WOA will request assistance from the Aronnax, sometimes both organizations are striving for the same things and sometimes they find themselves working at cross-purposes.

The WOA is a global protection agency, a United Nations for the sea. The organization often crosses paths with the Nekton family. It is represented by a blue wave insignia.

COMMANDER PYROSOME

The WOA is headed up by Commander Pyrosome. Those around her both respect and fear her authority. Pyrosome doesn't like having to work with 'civilians' – she only calls on the Nektons for help when she has no other option.

DIFFICULT HISTORY

Kaiko struggles to co-operate with the Commander. Once, a long time ago, she was a respected member of the WOA herself, but she soon found that she couldn't work for Pyrosome, or such a rigid organization.

UNRULY NEKTONS

The WOA has some stringent rules and, as the organization has to answer to the governments of the world, it isn't completely autonomous. This means Commander Pyrosome has to compromise in ways that the Nektons never would.

THE GUARDIANS

The Nektons have always suspected that Nereus was more than just a rosy-cheeked old gentleman. In fact, he is a 'Guardian of Lemuria'. Nereus is directly descended from a long line of powerful protectors.

The city of Lemuria sank into the sea thousands of years ago. Its location is shrouded in mystery. The Guardians know that there is something on Lemuria that needs to be kept hidden – at least until the day when the world is ready to rediscover it. Only Lemurian royalty can access this object, and no descendant has been able to find it or reach it... so far.

TETHYS   **GLAUCUS**

The Guardians are a secret society with vast resources, wealth and influence throughout the world. Proteus was once head of this ancient fraternity, but he abused the enormous responsibility entrusted to him.

HISTORY OF THE GUARDIANS

When Lemuria crumbled into the sea, its people evacuated across the globe. Memories of the kingdom gradually faded as its citizens became part of other countries and cultures. However, in the city's final moments, scientists close to the royal family were charged with protecting the secret of Lemuria and the power that sank with it.

Guardians Today
Since then, the Guardians have existed, all around the world, in their hundreds. They have infiltrated governments and other places of authority, always watching for those who would search for Lemuria and disturb its fragile slumber.

PROTEUS

BRAIDED BEARD
Proteus' hair has been white longer than anyone can remember.

GUARDIAN ROBES
Lined with gold and decorated with ancient symbols.

LEMURIAN STAFF
The staff has a rare orb set within a triad at the top.

Proteus' shrewd judgement and great intellect earned him the very highest office amongst the Guardians of Lemuria. He cuts a striking and commanding figure, possessing a deep knowledge of the ancient secrets of the city.

However, it was revealed the former head of the Guardians was not interested in protecting Lemuria at all. Instead, he wanted to harness its unique power for himself, and was even willing to use Ant Nekton and his family to get to it. When Proteus' treachery was discovered, he was cast out of the Guardians in disgrace.

DATA FILE

AGE:	Unknown
HEIGHT:	183 cm
LIKES:	Knowledge and power
DISLIKES:	Being outwitted, especially by a child like Ant Nekton
KIT:	Unknown

CLASSIFIED INTEL
Proteus has aligned himself with Alpheus Benthos, but who is using who?

"Some secrets should remain secret."

THE SECRETS OF LEMURIA

Lemuria was once a proud seafaring society, the greatest civilisation of its age. Its scientists and sailors developed many artefacts that now lie hidden, deep down beneath the waves. These artefacts could provide clues to the future.

IRON CASKET
Preserves the records within.

THE CHRONICLE OF THE DEEP

Over the centuries, as they watched for signs of Lemuria, the Guardians recorded strange sea events and phenomena in a parchment known as the 'Chronicle of the Deep'. The Chronicle is written in Lemurian, both to further hide the knowledge it contains and to keep the language alive. This irreplaceable document is now in the hands of the Nekton family. Will has been studying Lemurian for years. There is still more work for him to do in order to decipher all of the messages locked inside.

Lemurian Symbols
The Nektons are not yet able to read Lemurian. Its symbols and hieroglyphs are famously difficult to translate.

Race For Knowledge
Will is not the only one trying to
unlock the secrets of Lemuria.
Alpheus Benthos is determined to
solve the puzzle first.

THE EPHEMYCHRON

A carved globe called the Ephemychron was
once the ultimate navigational tool of the
Lemurians. After the fall of the city, the device
was broken up into three pieces and hidden by
the Guardians. The Ephemychron was tuned
to Lemuria, so in theory, it could be used again
to find its hiding place. Ant Nekton brought
the three parts of the Ephemychron back
together again.

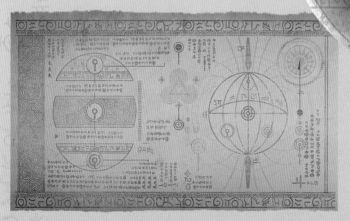

Blueprint Of The Blue
Orienting the Ephemychron to
the stars and constellations
reveals a map of the world.
Could this be the map
that will lead Ant to
Lemuria itself?

AN ANCIENT QUEST

When it comes to Lemuria, there seem to be more questions than answers... And yet, whatever the truth might be, Ant is at the very heart of it. Nereus believes that the youngest Nekton is the key to finding the city.

Could this be a mystery that Ant was born to solve? He found the pieces of the Ephemychron without even looking – it was almost as if the artefacts found him instead. Nereus is not deterred. His quest for Lemuria has taught him one important lesson – sometimes to see clearly you have to stop looking.

Time Turner
Lemurian artefacts are covered with symbols, codes and numbers. Gazing into these rare documents is like peering through a window to the past.

Place Of Wonder
Astonishing things
happen when Ant puts
the Ephemychron back
together. Dazzling stars and
planets align themselves
around the globe.

FOLLOW THE MAP
The Ephemychron's
map marks out many
ancient undersea sites.
The Nektons are on a
quest to seek out these
locations, eliminating
each one as they go.
Eventually, they hope
that the map will lead
them all the way to
Lemuria itself.

"Nekton family, set sail ..."

CHAPTER 6

CREATURES OF THE DEEP

NEKTON ECOLOGY

Will and Kaiko have taught their children that under the ocean every living creature and plant matters. The sea is the key to the future of our planet, and the Nektons have promised to play their part in preserving it.

When they're not assisting the WOA or foiling pirate plots, the Nektons dedicate their time to marine research. They understand that guarding animal habitats, identifying new species and reducing pollution is just as important as the most daring sea rescue. Expeditions in the Rover and Knights allow the Nektons to study animal behaviour up close and learn even more about the fragile and spectacular ecosystem they call home.

PET PALS

Ant has always had a deep affinity with sea creatures. He can interact with underwater life in a way that anyone else might fear to. He loves all marine animals, but his pet fish Jeffrey has an extra special place in his heart.

PLESIOSAUR

When a volcano erupted off the coast of Greenland, strange reports began to emerge. Tides were disrupted and fishing boats disappeared. The locals began to panic about what could be lurking below. There was even talk of a dragon sighting!

The truth was even more terrifying than the locals imagined – a giant leviathan called a plesiosaur. The creature had been hidden for years inside a sea trench, only emerging after seismic activity reopened the rift. The beast was vast, unpredictable and very, very dangerous.

TAPERED TAIL
The shape allows a plesiosaur to change direction quickly.

CAMOUFLAGE
Mottled stripes and markings hide a plesiosaur in cold waters.

TITANIC SIZE
At 108 metres long, the leviathan breaks all the records.

MEGA JAWS
A plesiosaur uses its impressive bite to confront prey head-on.

EYE TO EYE

The Shadow Knight looked miniscule when it swam up to meet the plesiosaur. The sheer size of the beast took Ant's breath away, scoring an unprecedented 11 on his Scare-O-Meter! The plesiosaur appears to be a solitary creature, but there could be others out there somewhere in the deep.

KEEPER OF SECRETS

This was not the first human encounter with a plesiosaur. Nereus told the Nektons that he had seen the creature before, revealing that Will's parents had also met the leviathan. The plesiosaur displayed a unique instinct for guarding Lemurian secrets. Something important was being kept inside its hidden lair. This is the place where Ant was destined to discover the Chronicle of the Deep.

COLOSSAL SQUID

MANTLE
Wider and deeper than any other kind of squid.

20-20 VISION
The squid has the largest eyes of any creature on Earth.

BEAK AND MOUTH
A parrot-like beak is hidden beneath arms and tentacles.

HOOKED TENTACLES
Each sucker is lined with tiny teeth.

Here Comes Trouble
When you've got an appetite like a colossal squid, the Rover looks like a tasty snack.

Ant thought that all his dreams had been answered when the Nektons came across a rare colossal squid. It marked the first time that one had ever been seen alive – a ginormous moment for science and the planet. Ant could not wait to make the most of the encounter, but he needed to approach with extreme care.

The squid showed itself to be intimidating, and potentially aggressive. It was willing to attack and eat nearly anything! The creature could expertly catch prey with its tentacles and then draw it towards its beak. The lights of the Aronnax seemed to mesmerise the creature, but not in a good way...

CLEVER AND COLOSSAL

The squid proved itself to be intelligent, working as part of a larger group. It pretended to play dead to lure in Ant and Fontaine.

GET INTO THE LIGHT

Ant quickly worked out that super-sized squid are aggravated by light. The molluscs are used to living at depths of over 2,000 metres, in an environment that is completely dark. This makes them acutely photosensitive. They also have one fear – whale song. It took a school of sperm whales to scare the squid away from the Nektons.

GIANT SEAHORSE

Ant was thrilled when he filmed a large and mysterious creature with ribbon-like fins on his underwater camera. It turned out to be wilder and more beautiful than anyone could imagine...

CAMERA SHY
Lives in deeper coastal waters, away from human activity.

MULTI-DIRECTIONAL FINS
Unlike other fish, this species can swim horizontally or upright.

ELONGATED SNOUT
Hydrodynamic head allows it to probe holes and small spaces.

IRRIDESCENT MARKINGS
The seahorse shimmers as it moves through water.

FRIEND OR FOE?

The TV monster hunter, Devil Daniels, tried to make out that a giant seahorse was attacking the people living on remote Tweed Island. The truth couldn't have been more different – the creature was timid, shy and gentle. Instead of harming others, it showed rare intelligence and compassion, moving to save rather than injure those around it.

Leap Of Faith
The giant seahorse is able to use its two sets of fins to rapidly thrust its entire body above the surface of the water.

Unspoken Connection
The giant seahorse forged a peculiar friendship with Ant Nekton. It instantly sensed that he could be trusted.

MEGALODON

There are big fish... and then there are BIG FISH. The Nektons were first alerted to the existence of a giant, supposedly extinct, shark when the WOA reported groups of sea creatures rushing through the ocean in a state of high alert.

The clusters of sea creatures were moving fast because they were running away. The cause? A megalodon migration. A herd of terrifying sharks was traversing the ocean, hunting out food. And when it came to diet, they weren't choosy. Anything and everything was getting snapped up in their enormous jaws.

Strange Migration
The Nektons discovered that megalodons cross the sea in search of new hunting grounds, possibly to feed their unborn babies.

RUDDER-LIKE TAIL
The megalodon makes a zigzag motion in the water.

DORSAL FIN
Stabilizes the fish against rolling, and assists sudden turns.

SHARP JAWS
Multiple rows of teeth are used to attack large prey, including whales.

AHEAD OF ITS TIME

Meeting a megalodon was a big surprise – the creature should have been extinct for 2.6 million years! Its ancestors were the single biggest predator on the planet, right at the top of the prehistoric food chain. Its closest modern relative is the great white shark.

Won't Stop, Can't Stop

Just like the great white, the megalodon was constantly on the move. Ant just had to make sure that he moved even faster!

GIANT CROCODILE

The Nektons were exploring an underwater cave system searching for fossils when they found something much more compelling. A giant egg was hiding deep down in the network of underground chambers – an egg that was ready to hatch.

When the egg cracked, the Nektons came face to face with a baby giant crocodile. A newborn reptile crying for food was not going to be on its own for long. A massive, and extremely angry, mother was only moments behind it!

SUPER SWIMMERS
Crocs grab their prey then drag them underwater to drown them.

MAMMOTH BODY
Adults are five times longer than the Nektons' jetboat.

RAZOR-LIKE TEETH
Combine with a sharp sense of smell to make the perfect predator.

LONG CLAWS
Used for ripping and tearing meat.

FEEDING TIME

Crocodiles can go for long periods without eating. Many survive on only 50 full meals per year. This rare giant sub-species was the same. Most of the time it appeared to be slow and lethargic, but when it did decide to strike for food, the force was sudden and shocking.

GIANT JAWS

A giant crocodile has a heart-stopping set of irregular teeth. They can be used for crushing huge objects, and also for delicately lifting and carrying its young. The tenderness of a nursing croc is astonishing to observe.

Devoted Mother

The Nektons discovered that a giant crocodile mother's aggressiveness is only equal to her desire to protect her babies. When she could be certain that Ant truly had her children's best interests at heart, she did not attack, instead withdrawing back into the cave system.

RAISED NOSTRILS
Allows breathing to continue whilst almost fully submerged in water.

DAMAGED SPINES
Evidence of many battles with rivals and prey.

GIANT HERMIT CRAB

When objects started to go missing from the tiny island of Hachoji-Kojima, the Nektons decided to investigate. Ant had a theory that aliens were responsible, but the real creatures proved even more weird and wonderful – a colony of giant hermit crabs.

VACANCY CHAIN

Hermit crabs need to replace their shells as they grow bigger, and this giant species was no different. When Ant and Fontaine followed the crabs in the Rover, they discovered stolen objects from the island lined up, from smallest to largest. It was a vacancy chain – homes waiting for sea creatures to try them on for size.

SENSITIVE ANTENNAE
Long, thin feelers used for navigation.

EXOSKELETON
Shed every time the crab moults.

Eerie Blue Light
The giant hermit crabs were able to create their own light source. The crustaceans glowed extra brightly when they were under threat.

GIANT PINCERS
For defence, climbing and moving heavy objects.

LEG PAIRS
Used for walking and balancing the crab's heavy shell.

Pincer Power
These hermit crabs had evolved into formidable predators, using their pincers to crush solid metal. Even the Rover was at risk from their snap.

MANTIS SHRIMP

Compared to sharks and squid, shrimp might seem like small fry, but a group of mantis posed one of the biggest threats to the Nektons the family have ever encountered. Each mantis shrimp has a powerful appendage that it can use to punch and smash.

The mantis shrimp attacked the Aronnax in great numbers while the sub was voyaging through the Baltic Sea. The creatures reacted to the electrical pulse of the vessel, surrounding it on all sides. They appeared to be a mutated species, with enhanced powers strong enough to crack both glass and titanium.

GIANT EEL

If the Nektons had to sum the giant eel up in three words they would say, 'slippery', 'coiling' and 'hostile'. The rare creature dwells in inky-black waters, usually many leagues below even the deepest submarine route. The eel can be dangerous and hostile to humans.

This species finds peculiar spots to hide its eggs. One unlucky day, it chose the cracks and crannies of the pirates' vessel, the Dark Orca. The crew discovered that the giant eel is able to raise its head out of water for prolonged periods of time. It is unclear if the creature would do this if it wasn't desperate to save its babies.

"It's a super eel.
How big can it
be?"

GIANT TARDIGRADE

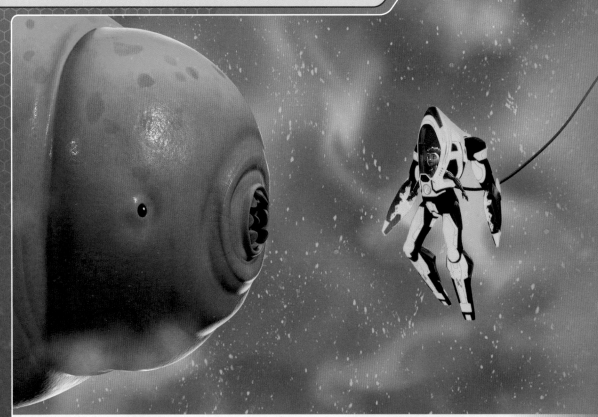

Regular tardigrades are smaller than the tip of a pin, but the giant kind occupy a completely different league! The strange sea beasts are also known as 'water bears'.

The Nektons came across floating giant tardigrades during a voyage to an alternate, pressureless environment. Perhaps it was this lack of pressure that enabled normally microscopic creatures to expand to the size of an elephant. More research is certainly needed to discover how the tardigrade has mutated. Despite their fearsome size, the giant species proved itself to be harmless.

It's A Mystery
The Nektons will need to revisit this location in order to better understand the giant tardigrade's habits and behaviour.

BAD LUCK FISH

BULBOUS FOREHEAD
Particularly prominent in the male of the species.

HEAVY-SET EYES
Sailors are sure they can't be trusted.

COLOURFUL FINS
In large shoals, the fish resemble swaying coral.

For centuries, ships have been sinking without explanation in the Sargasso Sea. Is the ocean cursed or are the superstitions true? Could the disasters all be down to a bad luck fish?

The creature's protruding forehead and bearded scowl looked scary enough, but fear has nothing to do with fact. Ships were sinking in the Sargasso because of the methane-rich waters, not because of any bad luck fish. The mystery was solved!

Meet Jeffrey
Ant's pet was wary of the newcomer in his tank. Even Jeffrey believed that the tales were true!

GIANT CLAM

A family diving trip in the Cook Islands led the Nektons into a field of unique gigantic clams. Ant was delighted – this species was totally new to marine science! The colourful clams were resting in the sand next to an undersea volcano.

Kaiko soon worked out what had happened. The rich chemical nutrients coming up from volcano activity below had created the perfect food chain. In those conditions the clams could keep growing and growing. The only threat to the molluscs growing inside was the prospect of an eruption raising the water temperature.

Moving Mountains
When a volcano nearby became active, Ant and his family were tasked with moving the clams to a safer site.

ENCRUSTED SURFACE
Forms a habitat for smaller plants and animals.

CRINKLE FIT
The giant clam has at least four folds in its outer shell.

HINGE
Permits the clam to shut, guarding the pearl inside.

HIDDEN FOOT
Burrows into the sand, rooting the clam to the spot.

BIOLUMINESCENTS

GLOWING LURE
Entrances anyone who gets too close.

IMMENSE JAWS
Swallow unsuspecting victims in one, large bite.

Many marine species use bioluminescence – the ability to light up in the dark. These are the occupiers of the Midnight Zone, a deep, barren place at the bottom of the sea.

The Nektons have to research these creatures with care. The light they create has an enchanting, hypnotic quality, drawing divers into a trance-like state. It's a trick for attracting prey to eat. And the angler fish is the absolute master.

Eyes On You
When Ant switched the Shadow Knight into stealth mode, the angler fish was drawn towards it.

DOLPHINS AND WHALES

Ant and Fontaine are mammals, just like the dolphins and whales they have swum with ever since they were little. They all love to play together, laugh and communicate.

Ever since Fontaine developed the Mimic Knight, she has been able to integrate even more closely with the dolphin pods that like to approach the Aronnax. She and Ant have rescued stranded orca and even Solar Skied alongside breaching killer whales. As well as having fun, the Nektons have learned lots!

LET'S CHAT

Whales and dolphins can't use words, but they are master communicators! Kaiko has taught Ant and Fontaine how to listen out for the resonant sounds made by different species, but their meaning remains a mystery.

MOBY-DICK

Devil Daniels created an Internet storm when he claimed to have discovered the real Moby-Dick, a wild and uncontrollable white whale described in the famous novel by Herman Melville. It was up to the Nektons to guide the leviathan to safety.

Firm Friends

The Nektons have taken whale-watching to a whole new high. Ant is especially fond of sperm whales. They are loyal, courageous and affectionate towards humans.

The White Whale

The real Moby-Dick was more magnificent than the Nektons had even imagined. It had been living for hundreds of years.

THE MONUMENTIALS

As Lemuria's trade routes expanded, they began to come into contact with giant sea creatures of the age known as Monumentials. These leviathans were mostly benign creatures.

The largest, however, was in no way benign. A force of great destruction roamed the seas in those days. It was known as the Terror. In an effort to take back control, Lemurian scientists developed a device that put all of the Monumentials into a deep slumber. Now, centuries later, could these sleeping beasts finally be awakening?

Giant Sea Worm
No one knows how this Monumential became imbedded behind the Denmark Strait's waterfall, but the Nektons suspect that it burrowed into the seafloor many years ago.

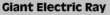

Giant Electric Ray
This mega-beast is able to harness and emit vast amounts of electricity up and out of the water. It emerged near the 'Everlasting Storm', off the coast of Venezuela.

Giant Kraken
As large as a city, the complete scope of the Kraken is almost too big for man to fathom. The Nektons discovered this Monumential imprisoned behind massive stone gates.

TARTARUGA

At first the Nektons thought they were visiting an island. And then the island started to move! The maps weren't wrong – instead the family had encountered a new, epic Monumential.

The island was a vast sea creature. Tartaruga had been in hibernating for centuries, but now it was starting to stir. The name means 'turtle' in Portuguese and Italian, suggesting that whoever gave the island its name knew that it was really a giant, floating sea turtle. The creature is so huge, the inner folds of its limbs form inlets and caverns that have been explored over the years. The question is why exactly did Tartaruga decide to wake up? Maybe the Monumential activity happening across the world is linked in some mysterious way...

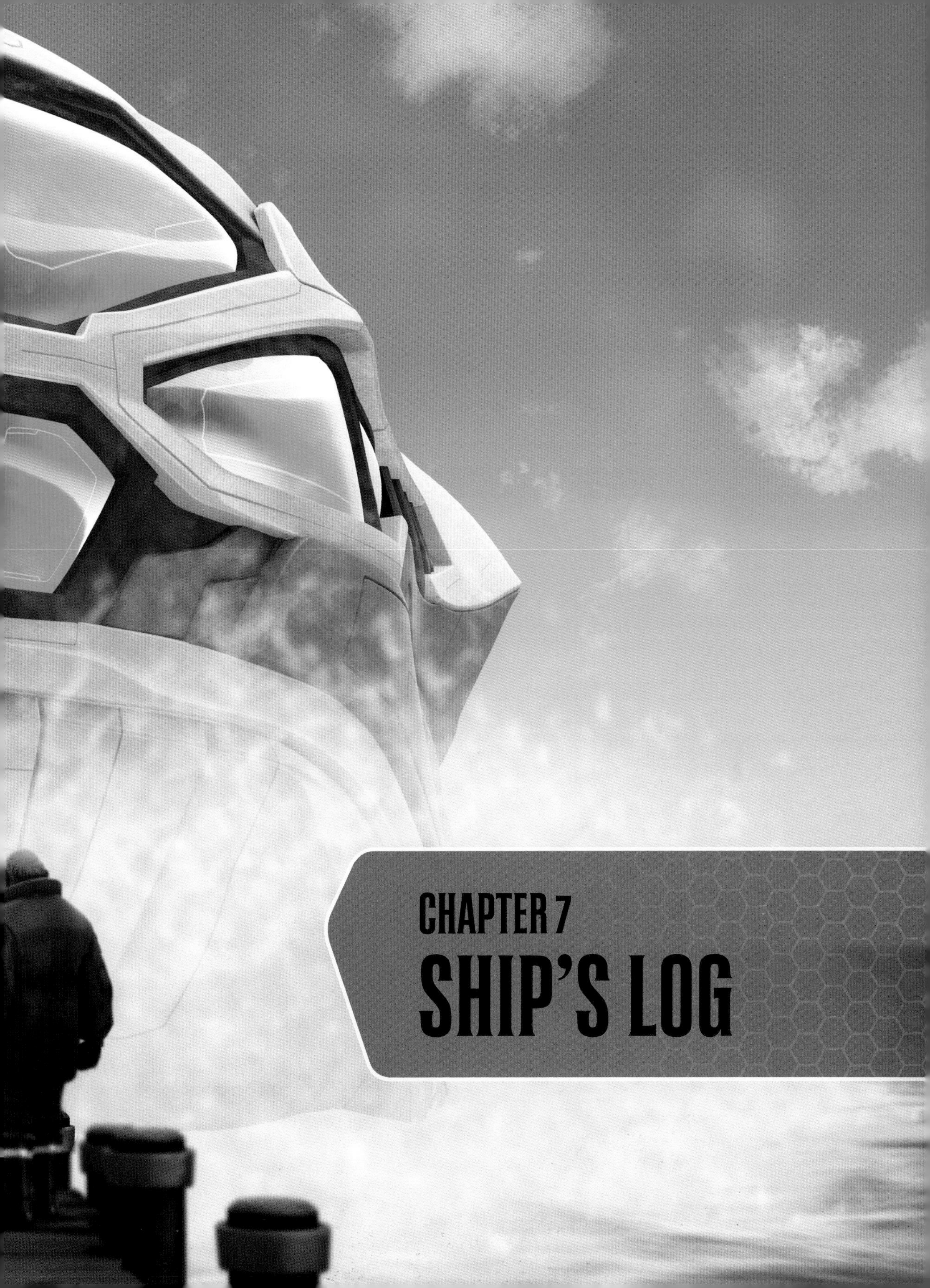

CHAPTER 7
SHIP'S LOG

PIRATE BATTLES

Will Nekton keeps meticulous records of his voyages in the Aronnax. Each data file is backed up with digital pictures in the ship's online log. It's here that he records sea rescues, jaw-dropping wildlife encounters and dealings with rotten pirates.

Captain Hammerhead and his crew work hard to thwart and obstruct the Nektons' missions. The Dark Orca has a bad habit of looming out of gloomy waters at just the wrong time. In the past the pirates have stolen rare artefacts, mounted raids on the Aronnax and even tried to kidnap the Nekton kids.

Captive!
When the pirates made Ant and Fontaine their prisoners on the Dark Orca, Smiling Finn was put on guard duty. It didn't take the Nektons long to escape.

Knight Fight

Captain Hammerhead has always been jealous of the Nektons' Knights. He dreamed up the 'Super Knight' in a bid to take them on.

Copy That

When he saw Fontaine's agile Mimic Knight, the Captain plotted to get a diving suit of his own. He forced Professor Fiction to build one for him.

POWER STRUGGLE

When pirates want something, they will do whatever it takes to get it. Captain Hammerhead demanded that his Knight should be big and strong enough to beat the Nektons in the water. The Super Knight was certainly larger than the Mimic, but it was never going to be a match for Fontaine and her family.

FACING FEARS

When you're a Nekton, showing great courage is just part of the territory. Every time the family ventures out of the Aronnax, their knowledge and skills are put to the test. Their lives depend on thinking fast and making good decisions.

Will's records recount some unbelievable dives. The Nektons have swum through trenches, explored kelp forests and got swept up in whirlpools. They have even been plunged into a blue hole – a deep sinkhole way out in the middle of the ocean. Entering that abyss was easy. Escaping was not.

Mimic Octopus
The blue hole proved to be a treacherous place. A rare mimic octopus used its skills to present the Nekton crew with mirror images of themselves.

WHO GOES THERE?

Some dives reveal rare, but deadly treasures. Kaiko was out shark-spotting when she found the entrance to a mysterious ancient temple that had been hidden for centuries. The Nektons didn't hesitate to jump in and explore.

BEWARE THE SENTINELS

The temple was guarded by stone sentinels, but when sunlight shone down through the water, they appeared to ripple and move. The sentinels were covered with poisonous stonefish. Ant and his family had to get out, fast!

PRESERVE AND PROTECT

Will and Kaiko have written many essays and papers about their conservation work. Ant and Fontaine are just as determined to create a bright future for the ocean, even if that means saving the world one habitat at a time.

When friends called the Nektons asking them to help save a rare species of tortoise, they didn't hesitate. The family were charged with protecting Lonesome Jim, the last male Galapagos tortoise of its kind in existence. The animal needed to be transported to a place where he could find a mate.

Extra Threat
Sebastian Conger is just one of the poachers trading ocean creatures. He made a bid to steal Lonesome Jim, but he underestimated his adversaries.

Look And Learn
Junior Nektons often come aboard the Aronnax to learn about saving the seas.

WHALE MIGRATION

The Junior Nekton fan club has got members all over the world. Once a group of club competition winners were invited to come and watch a sperm whale migration. Ant couldn't wait to describe every step of the process.

MAKE IT SAFE

The Junior Nektons didn't just see a migration – they witnessed a rescue, too! Ant used the White Knight to save a whale calf that was getting dragged down through the water in a tangle of lobster pot nets.

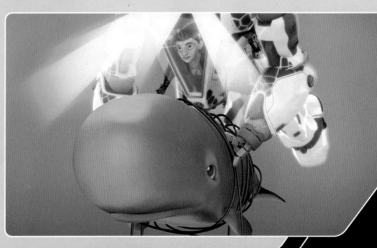

MAN AND MONSTERS

In his daily log, Will has described nearly every kind of sea creature, but every so often one appears that is bigger, fiercer and more terrifying than anything anyone has ever seen before!

Mega-beast
Near a Japanese island, the Nektons encountered a giant creature that was marching across the seafloor.

MOVIE MADNESS

The Nektons had no explanation for the havoc being wreaked – the furious marcher didn't look like any normal sea creature. The truth soon came out, however. The monster was a mechanical movie prop, created by the Nektons' old pal Kenji Nakimura! Together the crew managed to finally stop the robot in its tracks.

OFF THE CHARTS

The Monumentials make Kenji's monster look like small fry. The Nektons' first brush with the Giant Sea Worm was a life or death encounter – the family found themselves trapped inside the mega-beast's mighty gut.

Inside Out
The Sea Worm's vast stomach was filled with strange isopods, over-sized parasites floating through the rushing water.

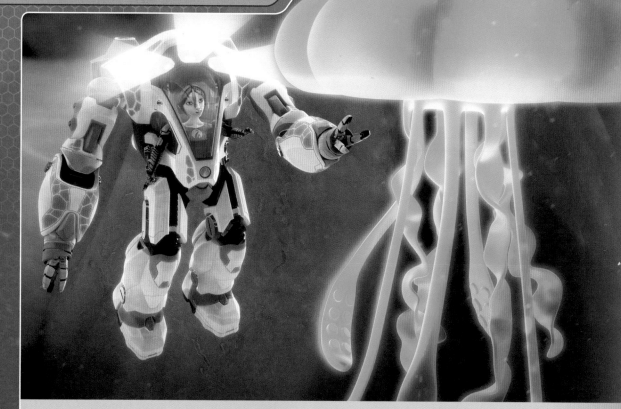

Always Watching
Nereus observed the Nektons carefully. Did he know more than he admitted about the challenges they faced?

The sea is deep, but sometimes strange lights do shine in the darkness below. Some of these phenomena can be easily explained, others are more mysterious. Will Nekton has chronicled many eerie experiences...

The day the Nekton family discovered the Ephemychron, they faced a unique and dangerous test. A strange maelstrom threatened to drown them all, then a zone of turbidity reduced the visibility down to zero. And as if that wasn't hard enough, next three huge, glowing jellyfish appeared. The jellyfish were robots, programmed to consume the entire Nekton family.

Shine A Light

When Ant put all the pieces of the Ephemychron together, it was transformed. Stars and symbols began to shimmer in the air.

FROM THE STARS

Ant held in his hands the key to solving the secrets of the sea. The Aronnax became the centre of a dazzling orbit of stars and constellations, rotating in perfect harmony around the glowing Ephemychron. The lights were clues in Ant's quest, but where they would lead him was a still a mystery.

GHOSTS FROM THE PAST

Keeping a log is important on any vessel, it stands as a record of history – of what has gone before. The Nektons are not the first sailors to have made the ocean their home. The past creates ripples that still echo today.

Once, in the dead of night, the Aronnax almost collided with a strange glowing underwater vessel. Back at the Nektons' island base, Ant found a book about Alessandro De Salazar, a nineteenth century inventor. The vessel they almost hit looked a lot like De Salazar's greatest invention – a wooden submarine built 200 years ago!

THE PHANTOM SUB

Ant was puzzled. De Salazar's sub couldn't possibly still exist, let alone be in working order. The youngest Nekton drew the only obvious conclusion. The vessel had to be a ghost! The next question was even more obvious. Who, in the seven seas, could be piloting it?

CHILD WITH KRAKEN

At times the past can confuse as much as it is enlightens. When the Nektons salvaged a priceless lost artwork from a ship called the Minerva, Ant could not believe his eyes. The boy in the picture was holding the Ephemychron!

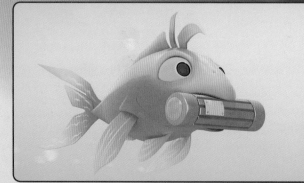

Living History
The painted boy looked spookily similar to Ant Nekton. Everyone around him sensed that he might have a part to play in history, too. Even Jeffrey understood that Ant was important!

MYTHS AND LEGENDS

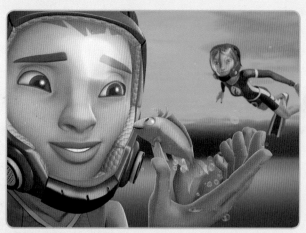

Follow Me
The song of the siren didn't only catch Ant's attention, Jeffrey also heard the haunting call drifting through the water. The little fish swam after the sound.

When they were little, Ant and Fontaine used to love being told stories about the sea. Today Will's log recounts events that are even more extraordinary. All myths have to start somewhere!

SONG OF THE SIREN

Ant, Fontaine and Jeffrey were out exploring a coral reef when they first heard a strange, singing sound. Ant believed that the noise came from a siren – a magical creature trying to lure sailors to their doom. The truth was quite different. The song was coming from a brand new species of whale called Blue 52.

INTO THE MAZE

The Ephemychron once directed Ant, Fontaine, Kaiko and Will towards an underwater maze. As soon as the Nektons entered it the walls began to shift and move, trapping them inside. The maze was full of tricks.

MEET THE MINOTAUR

The centre of the maze held another threat – there was a minotaur inside. Even more curious than the one of legend, the creature had a bull's head, a man's body and a shark's tail. Sometimes the truth can be stranger than fiction!

CHAPTER 8
UNCHARTED WATERS

MAKING THE SHOW

How does a production crew go about making a sensational show like *The Deep*? Creating an underwater world filled with stunning subs and spectacular sea creatures is a massive undertaking! Every episode is carefully conceived and then painstakingly brought to life by a team of animators, artists, writers, voice actors and more.

SCRIPT TO SKETCH

Every new episode starts with a script, setting out the lines each character will say. A script for *The Deep* is usually around 30 pages long. Once the production team are happy, the script is sent to an artist who will work up the storyboard. A storyboard is a visual guide for the production team to follow, showing what will appear on the screen for each shot. It takes eight weeks for the artist to put each storyboard for an episode of *The Deep* together.

SEA SOUNDS

As soon as the script is finalised, the voice actors can record the audio for each episode. Storyboard artists prefer to work with the final audio, but at times they have to draw without it and imagine how the characters will deliver their lines.

ANI-MAGIC

The journey from storyboard to screen is a complex but super-fun process! Up to eight animators work on each episode, with a lead animator and a director to guide them. The animation stage is all done using sophisticated computer programs, but it still requires a huge amount of patience and artistry. The animation work takes ten weeks per episode. Afterwards a team of lighting artists and the rest of the crew need around a month to complete each episode.

DATA FILE

AVERAGE NUMBER OF SHOTS PER EPISODE:	415
NUMBER OF FRAMES PER EPISODE:	30,476
NUMBER OF DRAWN PANELS PER STORYBOARD:	1,500–2,200
PEOPLE INVOLVED IN MAKING THE SHOW:	150
TIME TAKEN TO CREATE EACH EPISODE:	40 weeks

CUT!

The Deep production team are constantly researching, sketching and thinking up ideas for the show. The ocean is a vast place and there are always new challenges for the Nektons to face and conquer!

Ideas, storylines and sets can be reworked countless times before they officially become part of The Deep and its world. Everyone on the production team knows the characters so well, they talk about the Nektons as if they are real people. It's like having a shared, extended family! Some concepts don't quite make it to screen, but they are always useful – a launch pad for even more amazing episodes of The Deep...

HERE BE DRAGONS

In the very first episode of The Deep, Ant found the Chronicle of the Deep. This is a concept drawing of the first proposed hiding place – an old shipwreck. This set was never built, however. Later the production team decided to build the Chronicle of the Deep into a stone pedestal. This helped suggest that the Chronicle was buried much longer ago, before the shipwreck had even landed on the seafloor.

A LEMURIAN MYSTERY

This is a concept painting for an eerie blue hole deep below the surface. The idea was that the hole contained an ancient Lemurian site, but this location was never used in the series.

A PLACE FOR PIRATES

Sailors beware the pirates' lair! This very cool concept painting is an early imagining of what Captain Hammerhead's home might have looked like. The Orcan base sits on a stormy sea, surrounded by jagged rocks and shipwrecks. The production team ultimately decided to scrap this set because it wasn't needed – the pirates' home is the Dark Orca submarine.

WAITING IN THE WINGS

It's not just sets that come and go, characters can change and develop, too. Trish is a reporter who appears in the original graphic novels of *The Deep*. She has been left out of the TV episodes so far because the Nektons very rarely have adventures on land.

SHAPING THE CHARACTERS

Aquanauts and pirates, Guardians and rogues – every cast member on *The Deep* has been through many stages of development before transforming into the animated character that we're all familiar with.

The pencil sketch turnarounds underneath were given to a modelling artist to begin the computer-generated sculpture for the animation. The team also included an early design of Fontaine for height reference. Notice how the green stripes on her wetsuit are different from how they appear in the series.

Pirate Gold
These are some of the trinkets that Madeline has collected on her piratey adventures!

'MAD' MADELINE

This is an almost complete design for the youngest crew member on the Dark Orca. Madeline's hair was revised and a few details were adjusted before she went into production.

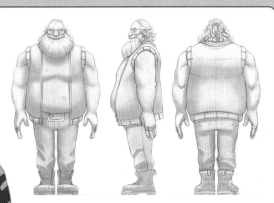

Pencil Sketch Turnarounds
In order to do their job, the model artists need to know exactly what a character looks like from every angle.

CAPTAIN HAMMERHEAD

After drafting several versions of Hammerhead's design, this is the one that everyone on *The Deep* production crew finally selected. The team wanted the Captain to look bad, but also different to the typical pirate look that people are used to seeing on TV and in the movies.

Captain In Colour
This is the completed computer-generated model, nearly ready for animation production.

BUILDING THE ARONNAX

Notice how the Aronnax was designed with only three chairs. Kaiko's captain chair is in the middle, Fontaine's is on the left and Will's is on the right. Ant doesn't sit still very long, so he doesn't have his own chair.

THE BRIDGE

These are the nearly finished designs of the bridge on the Aronnax. The windows were designed to be big enough to see plenty of different kinds of creatures, both large and small. It also had to look high tech – like something that might appear in a spaceship.

Position Guide
A floor layout shows how characters will move throughout the space, and where each of the different high tech items will be placed.

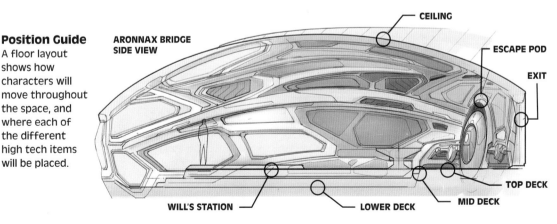

ARONNAX BRIDGE SIDE VIEW

CEILING

ESCAPE POD

EXIT

WILL'S STATION

LOWER DECK

MID DECK

TOP DECK

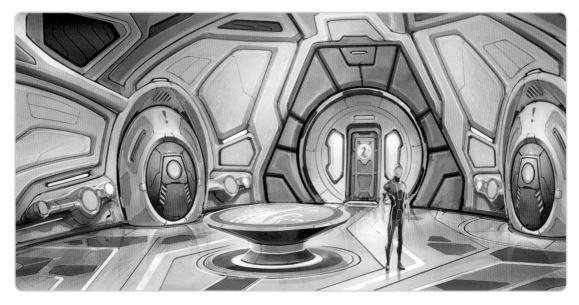

SPOT THE NEKTON

The rough sketch of Will is included in the picture so that the CG (computer graphics) modeller can work out how big to build the set.

Looking Down

This is called a floor layout design. It shows a bird's eye view of the bridge.

DESIGNING THE KNIGHTS

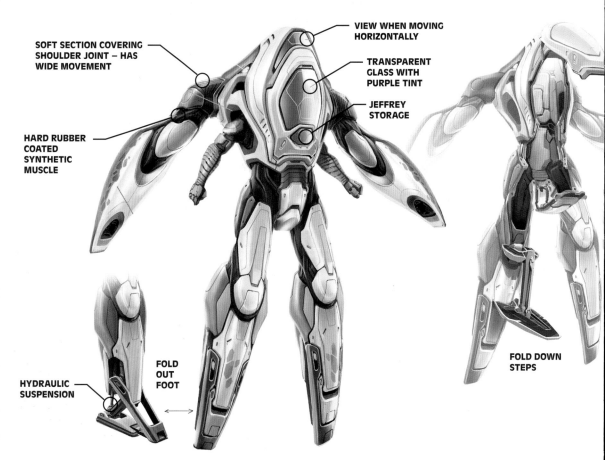

SOFT SECTION COVERING SHOULDER JOINT – HAS WIDE MOVEMENT

VIEW WHEN MOVING HORIZONTALLY

TRANSPARENT GLASS WITH PURPLE TINT

JEFFREY STORAGE

HARD RUBBER COATED SYNTHETIC MUSCLE

HYDRAULIC SUSPENSION

FOLD OUT FOOT

FOLD DOWN STEPS

This is the final design of the Shadow Knight that was supplied to the modelling department. The production crew wanted this diving suit to be inspired by real-life sharks.

The hydraulic elements in the drawings demonstrate how the feet can fold when standing is necessary, and form steps that allow Ant to climb up into the cockpit. These details help the modeller understand which parts of the Knight need to move.

Natural Predator
The Shadow Knight can be fast and stealthy in the water, just like a shark. It is also streamlined, which makes it clumsy on land.

Back View
A reverse angle of the Shadow Knight is also created in preparation for the 360° degree model.

ROUGH REAR

FIN

THRUSTER

THRUSTERS

THE MIGHTY MAG
The Mag Knight was specifically designed to be a big all-purpose diving suit, with chunky, durable parts. The look of the Knight and its bold, yellow markings were inspired by a giant hydraulic crane.

Moving Toolkit
The Mag Knight's capabilities were carefully plotted out at the very beginning. Sketches and designs were made for every function and part.

Ready For Action
These are the final front and rear designs for the Mag Knight, ready to go to *The Deep* modelling department.

INSIDE THE DARK ORCA

The look and feel of the Dark Orca could not be more different to the modern and airy Aronnax, and that's just how the production crew planned it. It is a dark, gloomy place built for skulking and scheming!

DARK ORCA PORTHOLES

These are porthole details given to the modeller to build on the inside and outside of the Dark Orca sub. Much of the submarine is designed to look like heavy steel, and the grey paint swatch has been provided as inspiration for this weathered steel look.

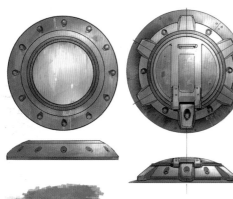

Glowing Glass
All the windows in the Dark Orca have a fiery orange glow.

TANK OF THE SEA

The windows were designed to give the Dark Orca the appearance of an armoured tank, which typically only has small slits for windows in order to protect against attacks. The pirates don't care that their submarine pollutes the ocean with oil and fuel, so everything about their ship also needed to look crude and rough.

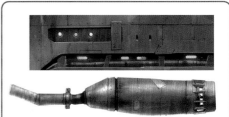

Scrap Metal
The exhaust pipes were drawn as if they were welded together from spare parts.

Dark Orca Bridge
This is the final colour design of the bridge on the Dark Orca. It is much smaller than the main deck of the Aronnax.

ROUGH TOUCH

A special artist was responsible for creating the finishes on the Dark Orca. Every colour, texture and detail was carefully designed to make the pirates' sub look realistic, as if it was covered in rusting metal.

CREATURE CONCEPTS

Every creature that dives into *The Deep* has been meticulously studied and researched by the production crew. Some animals are based on real species, some are inspired by myths and stories and others are pure fantasy!

TARTARUGA

This is the final design of the giant turtle known as Tartaruga. Every drawing for it needed to be highly finished. In the show, the Nekton family get *very* close to this enormous beast so every part of it had to be accurate.

Pencil Turnarounds
These are some of the 360° sketches that the modelling artist used to build the computer-generated giant crocodile.

Floating Island
Above the ocean surface, the turtle's shell resembles an uninhabited island. Only when seen below the sea is the creature revealed as a Monumential.

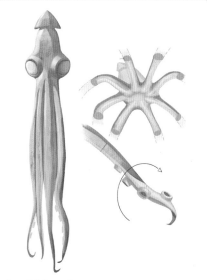

Squid Prank
In the Devil's Sea Mystery (S1 E5), Ant gets hit in the face by a mini squid. Here it is, down to the detail of its individual tentacles and suckers.

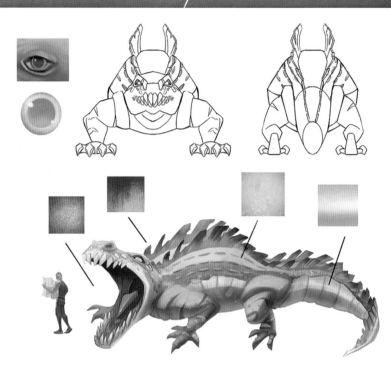

GIANT CROC

This snapping, tail-flicking beast makes a massive impact when it appears in *The Deep*! The colour action pose was created to show other production crew members how the reptile should move and animate. Will Nekton is included again so that the modeller knows exactly how big to make the croc.

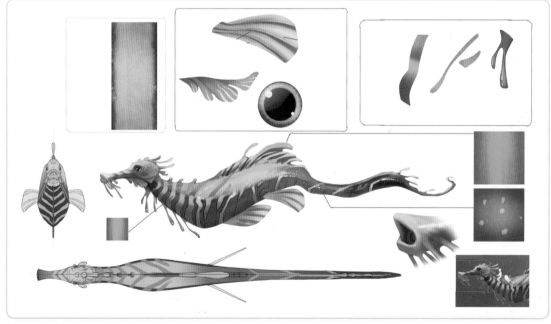

Giant Seahorse
This design was inspired by real-life seahorses. As they are very tiny, some elements had to be adapted to make this creature look much larger.

CREATURE CONCEPTS

The ocean is teeming with life, and the underwater world of *The Deep* is no different. A huge cast of fish, squid and other sea creatures appear in every show. Their naturalistic movement, sounds and behaviour help us to believe in the Nektons and share their passion for their astonishing undersea home.

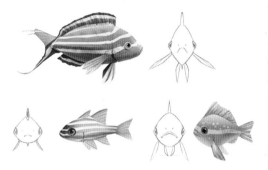

Some of the animals in *The Deep* function like human 'extras'. Although they are not key to the story, they swim by in the background to make the ocean setting look more realistic. Whenever a shoal of fish appears in the series, it is actually made up of the same fish duplicated many times.

Reef Fish

These stripy specimens are based on actual reef fish. In the series, the animators sometimes changed their colours to make them look like different fish.

PLESIOSAUR

Here are two giant plesiosaur design options that were put forward for the very first episode of *The Deep*. The crew chose to send the top design to the modeller to build. Although the selected creature was inspired by a real plesiosaur, it has been changed significantly so that it looks like an off-shoot species from the Plesiosauria family.

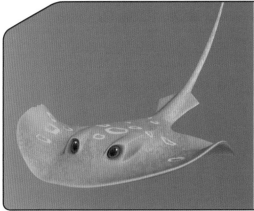

Stingray

The ocean is home to a dazzling variety of life, and *The Deep* needs to reflect this. This is the final computer-generated model of a generic stingray that was built to help populate the oceans in the show.

THE OCEAN DEEP

In *The Deep*, the ocean is a lead character in its own right! Every environment has to look intriguing and believable – whether it's an undersea volcano, a seaweed forest or a raging whirlpool.

In the first pirate episode, Dark Orca (S1 E2), the Nektons enter a treacherous cave. The final concept design for the entrance is shown at the top of the page. The orange areas on the image represent where the visual effects artists need to create the effect of hot lava.

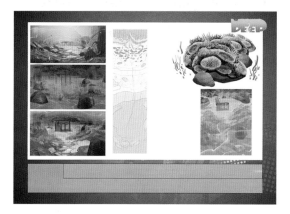

NO ACCIDENT

Every element in the background of a scene for *The Deep* has been carefully plotted out. The designs on this reef screen were used to help the crew know how and where to place the coral.

SHIPWRECKS

These are always creepy places! The Viking wreck above was featured in Loki's Castle (S1 E19). It is quite different to the unknown vessel submerged in the Sargasso Sea in the concept picture on the right. The remains of this craft appeared in Bad Luck Fish (S1 E21). The giant methane bubbles are created from rotting seaweed – so big and powerful that they might just sink a boat.

DESIGN ELEMENTS

These are the individual coral designs that were used to build the reef locations in the show. Whenever you spot more than one similar type of coral in *The Deep*, there's a good chance that it is the same piece of coral duplicated many times.

GLIMPSE THE FUTURE

So what new sets are the crew dreaming up for Team Nekton? It's time to take an exclusive peek into *The Deep* production files. Explore new zones in the Aronnax, watch Professor Fiction at work and check out some awesome new kit! None of these have been featured on the show, but that could be set to change...

INTO CARGO BAY

The Nektons store all their additional equipment in the cargo bay. When needed, robotic arms retrieve gear from the storage room doors that line the bay and then drop them down into the Moon Pool chamber. Can you spot the entrance to the chamber in the centre of the floor? The cargo bay hasn't been featured yet in the show, but hopefully it will make an appearance soon!

CONCEPT ARTWORK FOR UNDERWATER ACCESS INTO THE BAY

MAIN VIEW OF THE CARGO BAY

FONTAINE'S BEDROOM

Ever wondered where Fontaine goes to chill out and unwind? Up to now, viewers have only seen Ant's bedroom, but that could be set to change. These images are part of the concept work for Fontaine's space – check out the electric guitars and the rock poster on the wall. Her bedroom certainly looks a lot neater than Ant's!

EARLY PAINTING OF FONTAINE'S BEDROOM

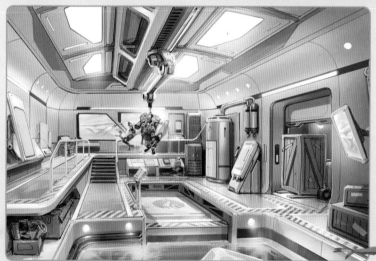

GOTTA FLY!

Who wouldn't want a ride on this hoverboard? This fantastic vehicle sketch showcases a new idea to help Ant get around even faster. The production team are hoping that the youngest Nekton might get to use the hoverboard for real in a future episode.

FICTION'S LAB

We all know that Professor Fiction works on the Nekton's secret base, but no one has been granted access inside... until now! This is a concept painting of the Prof doing his day job, with the help of a robotic arm. The scene is a mix of low and high tech. As well as flatscreen computers, the set is filled with crates, canisters and machinery.

SEASON THREE AND BEYOND...

Where will *The Deep* head next? The Nekton family's amazing underwater adventures are set to continue with new friends and familiar foes. Ant, Fontaine, Kaiko, Will and Jeffrey are in for close-up creature encounters, pirate wrangles and more than a few surprises.

Now the stakes are higher than ever as the aquanauts come face to face with more and more Monumentials – the vast, ancient and dangerous leviathans awakening all over the globe. And it all points to one place: the legendary civilization of Lemuria.

"The sea is deep and full of secrets."

DO YOU WANT MORE FROM THE DEEP?

The sea is full of secrets! Join the Nektons on their daring underwater adventures with more books all about _THE DEEP_, never before seen on screen!

THE DEEP STICKER ACTIVITY BOOK

The Nekton family are on a mission to shine light on the darkest extremes of the ocean! Packed with super submersibles, astonishing sea creatures and breath-taking Lemurian mysteries, this sticker activity book will take you on all the amazing aquatic adventures of _The Deep_!

THE DEEP BOOK 1 DRAGON RIDER

Something is seriously wrong in the South China Sea and the Nektons are on an urgent mission to save its ocean floor and sea creatures from poisonous gases and magma. But they don't expect to discover a mysterious creature in the depths. Could this be their toughest challenge yet?

THE DEEP BOOK 2 SELKIE WARRIOR

The Nektons have been caught in a cyclone! The family of daring underwater explorers manage to reach an island in the Arafura Sea. But something doesn't seem right; it looks like someone has been tampering with the Aronnax ... Soon they discover they have a new enemy – but will they be able to stop them?